On the Move

THE STORY OF A

TRUCK

D0198768

Kingfisher Books, Grisewood & Dempsey Ltd,
Elsley House, 24–30 Great Titchfield Street,
London W1P 7AD

First published in 1990 by Kingfisher Books

10 9 8 7 6

BRITISH LIBRARY CATALOGUING IN PUBLICATION DATA
Royston, Angela
    Truck.
    1. Lorries
    I. Title   II. Farman, John   III. Series
    629.224
ISBN 0 86272 540 2

With thanks to Keith Irving, Allport Freight Ltd, London

Edited by Veronica Pennycook
Designed by Ben White
Cover design by Terry Woodley
Phototypeset by Southern Positives and Negatives (SPAN),
Lingfield, Surrey
Printed in Spain

On the Move

THE STORY OF A

TRUCK

By Angela Royston

Illustrated by John Farman

Kingfisher Books

The truck in this story is an articulated truck. It has two parts, a tractor and a trailer. The trailer is like a huge box on wheels which is hooked up to the tractor and pulled along.

Trailer

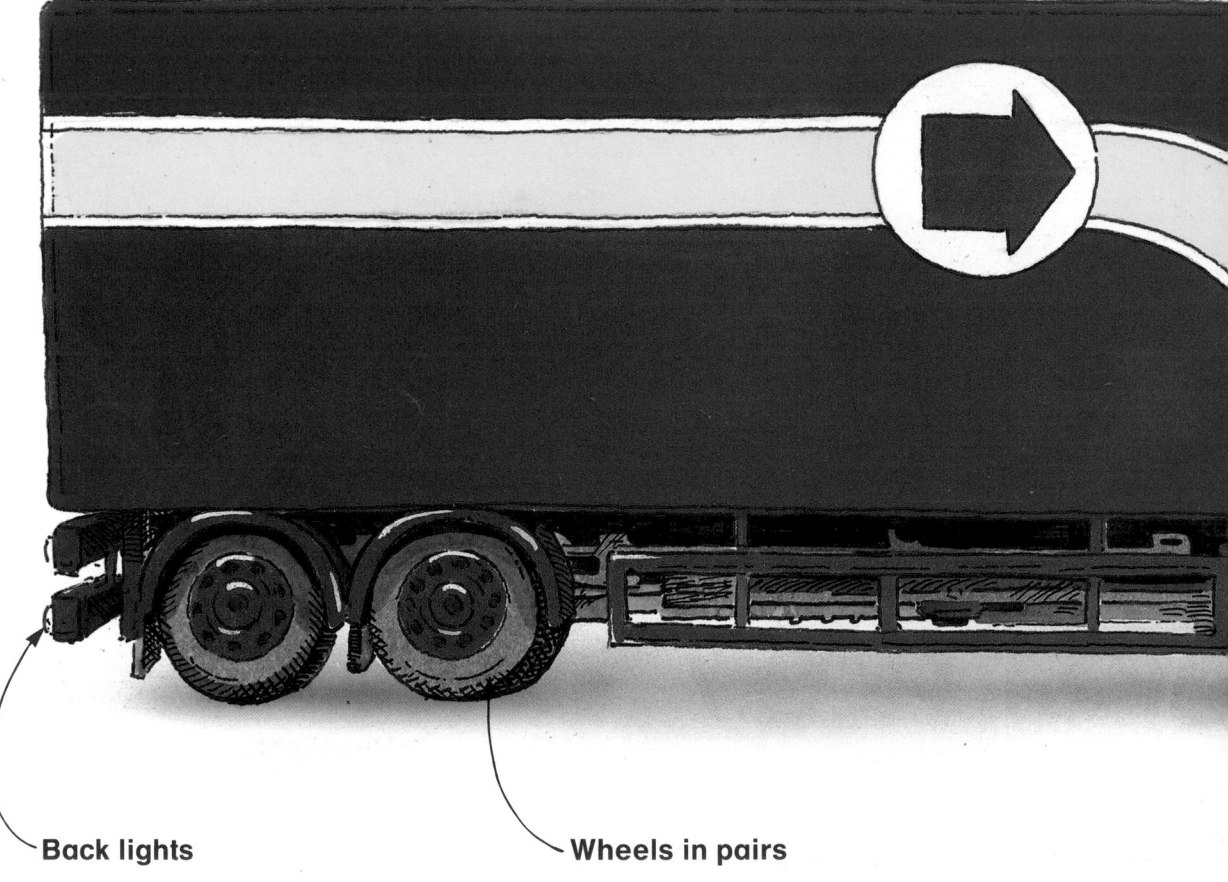

Back lights

Wheels in pairs

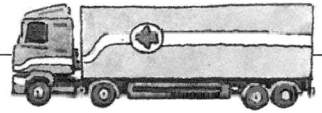

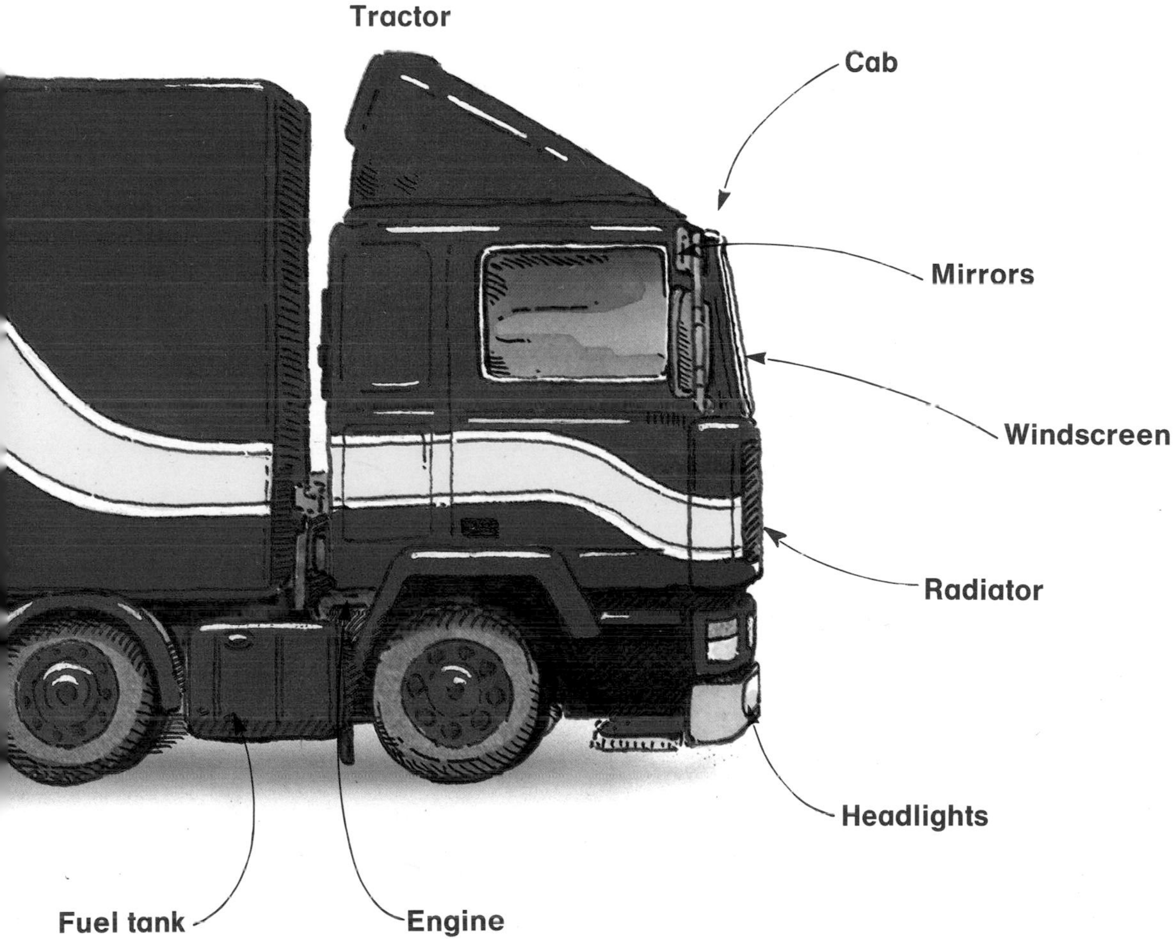

Tractor

Cab

Mirrors

Windscreen

Radiator

Headlights

Fuel tank

Engine

It is a cold, wet morning and the big truck is parked right over in the corner of the truck depot. Sam pulls on his cap and walks across the busy yard to his truck. He is a driver for the truck company and this morning he is taking his truck to the docks to deliver a load of medicines.

Other drivers are collecting their trucks too, and some wave to Sam as he walks by. The crates of medicine are already inside the trailer, so Sam checks there is enough water in the radiator and enough oil in the engine. Then he climbs into the cab and drives to the fuel pump to fill up with fuel.

Sam drives out of the depot and through the streets to the motorway. He changes gear again and again and the heavy truck slowly picks up speed. It is raining but the big windscreen and mirrors give him a good view of the motorway in front and behind.

When he reaches the port Sam turns off the motorway. The road he takes to the docks is narrow and a car is parked on the corner where Sam has to turn. First the tractor then the trailer turns, but the wheels along one side scrape the pavement.

A ship has just come in to the docks and is being unloaded. Sam drives over to the warehouse and puts on the brakes. They hiss loudly and the truck quickly comes to a stop. Sam climbs down and goes into the office. "Medicines for South America," he says as he passes over the delivery papers.

Sam watches as a forklift truck takes the crates off the trailer. A new load is then lifted up and rolled into the trailer. This time Sam is taking big bales of cloth to a depot in another city.

Sam has a long journey ahead, but as he drives out of the port he realizes that something is wrong with one of the wheels. He pulls into a layby and gets out. One of the tyres is flat. "Oh no!" he groans. "Must have torn it getting round that tight corner!"

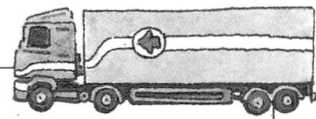

Using his mobile phone, Sam asks a truck tyre service to send out a mechanic. Then he gets out his lunch-box and settles down in the cab to wait.

When the mechanic arrives, he lifts the wheel off the ground with a special trolley jack. He uses a tool called an airgun to undo the nuts that hold the heavy truck wheel in place. The flat tyre is taken off and rolled to one side.

Sam fetches the huge spare wheel from under the tractor. He rolls it over to the mechanic and together they lift it into place.

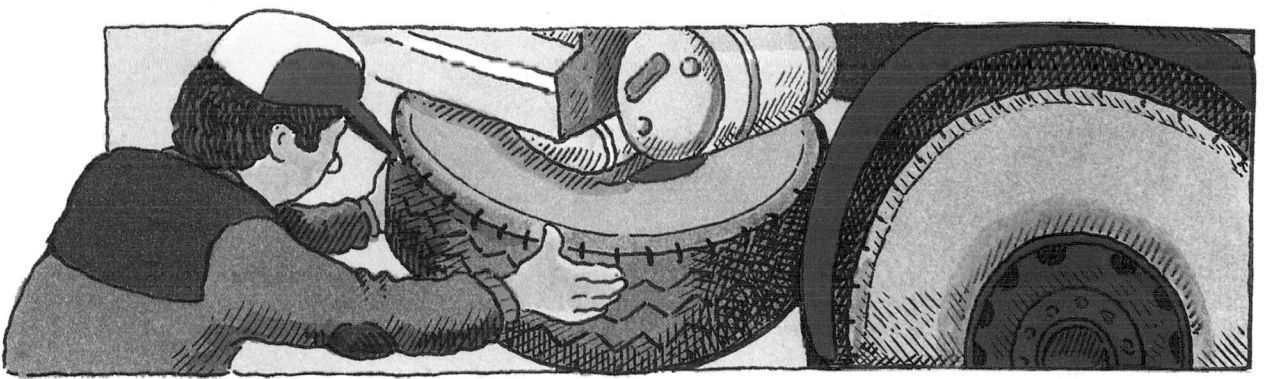

While the mechanic tightens up the wheel nuts, Sam puts the flat tyre away. Now he can carry on with his journey.

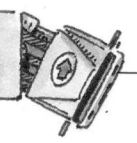

Sam still has a long way to go so he uses his CB radio to find out what other truck drivers know about the road ahead. They say there is snow further on. It is getting dark so Sam decides to stop at the next transport cafe.

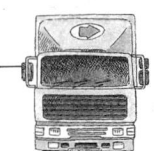

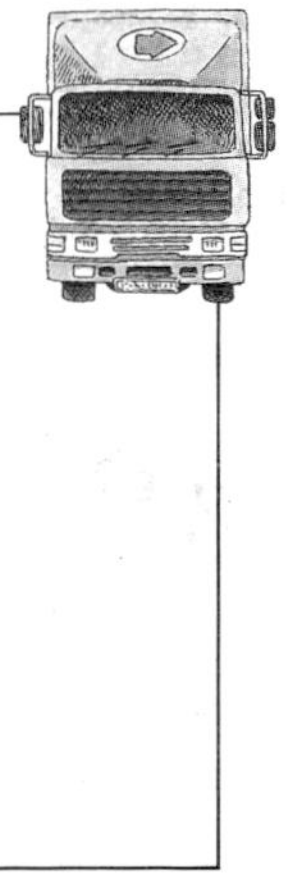

He eats in the cafe and then goes back to his cab to sleep. At the back of the cab is a cosy bunk bed. Sam climbs in and pulls the curtains together. His alarm clock will wake him early in the morning, ready for another day's driving.

During the night it begins to snow. Sam knows the mountain roads will be slippery, so he unhooks the trailer and fits snow chains around the tractor wheels to help them grip the road.

Later that morning he sees a long traffic jam on the other side of the road. A large truck has got stuck climbing a steep hill. "They'll be there for hours," thinks Sam. "I'm glad I put the chains on." He picks up his CB radio and tells other truck drivers to take a different road to avoid the traffic jam.

That afternoon Sam arrives at the depot where he is
to deliver the cloth. "Park the trailer over there,"
says Hugh, the foreman. Sam looks at the narrow
space between two other trucks. He will have to use
the tractor to edge the trailer in backwards.

He shunts backwards and forwards, slowly moving the trailer into the right position. At last Hugh shouts "OK!" and Sam turns off the engine with a sigh of relief. Then Hugh checks the load and signs the delivery papers.

Sam unhooks the tractor from the trailer. It will be unloaded later and vans will deliver the cloth to several shops. Hugh shows Sam another trailer. "This one has to go to the airport," he says. Sam gets into his cab and backs slowly up to it.

The jaw on the back of the tractor hits a large pin on the trailer and the two lock together. Sam climbs out and links up the coloured cables for the brakes and lights. "Just the fuel and oil to check and then I'll be off again," he says to Hugh.

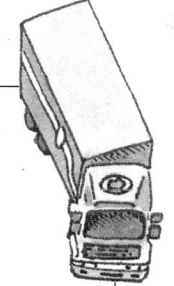

Some Special Words

Airgun A machine which works like a spanner, loosening and tightening nuts on bolts.

Bales Bundles. Cloth is often rolled into bales to be delivered.

Cable Strong wire. On trucks, the cables connect the lights and brakes between the tractor and the trailer.

CB radio Citizens' Band radio. Truck drivers can talk to each other on CB radio.

Depot A yard with warehouses and offices where trucks collect and deliver goods.

Docks A place in a harbour where ships are loaded and unloaded.

Foreman The person in charge of a depot.

Gears Cog wheels in car and truck engines which help control the car or truck's speed.

Jack A machine for lifting the wheel of a car or truck off the ground.

Layby A place at the side of the road where cars and trucks can pull over and stop.

Mechanic A person who looks after and mends machinery.

Motorway A wide road with several lanes.

Port A town by the sea with a harbour.

Radiator A tank of water. In a car or truck, water from the radiator flows in pipes around the engine to keep it cool.